Petit Our...
veut un c...

Hélène Serre ● Danièle Bour

bayard jeunesse

Ce soir, quand Papa Ours
rentre à la maison,
Petit Ours Brun crie :
– Papa ! Papa ! C'est Papa !

Plus tard, quand il entend
la clé dans la porte,
Petit Ours Brun dit :
— Maman, un bisou,
un bisou !

Petit Ours Brun et sa maman s'embrassent.
Maman Ours dit :
– Mmm, ça c'est la meilleure chose au monde !

Maman Ours a envie aussi
de retrouver Papa Ours.
Mais Petit Ours Brun
n'aime pas ça !

Petit Ours Brun
ne lâche pas sa maman.
Il dit : – Non, c'est ma maman
à moi !

Papa Ours ne cède pas.
Il rit : – Attends, Petit Ours,
un baiser d'amoureux,
c'est très précieux !

Puis Papa Ours prend
Petit Ours dans ses bras.
Petit Ours Brun est content,
entre son papa
et sa maman.

Découvre d'autres aventures de Petit Ours Brun :

Petit Ours Brun fait un bonhomme de neige

Petit Ours Brun aime compter

Petit Ours Brun se brosse les dents

Petit Ours Brun ne veut pas manger

Petit Ours Brun et les bisous

Petit Ours Brun va à l'école

Petit Ours Brun s'habille tout seul

Petit Ours Brun aime son papa

Petit Ours Brun aime sa maman

Petit Ours Brun va dormir

Petit Ours Brun sur le pot

Petit Ours Brun fait du vélo

Petit Ours Brun à la ferme

Petit Ours Brun et les pompiers

Petit Ours Brun réveille ses parents

Petit Ours Brun va à la bibliothèque

Cl...
to Spot

Illustrated by Lucy Semple

Designed by Sharon Cooper
Words by Kate Nolan

You can use the stickers to fill in the chart
at the back of the book, so you can keep
track of the clouds you have seen.

Sunny days

Cumulus fractus
These little shreds are pulled apart by air currents. Watch for them constantly moving and changing shape.

Cumulus humilis
Look for these fluffy white clouds on sunny summer days. They're sometimes called fair-weather cumulus.

Quite low in the sky

Cumulus mediocris
Cumulus humilis might grow into these bigger, darker clouds as the day goes on.

Sun

A huge, bright ball of burning gases. Remember never to look directly at it – you could damage your eyes.

Cirrus uncinus

These long, hook-shaped, wispy clouds can mean that windy weather is coming.

Cirrus clouds are very high up

Cirrus floccus

You might see lots of these rounded, woolly puffs spreading across the whole sky.

Storms and showers

Cumulus congestus

When you spot cumulus clouds building up so that they're taller than they are wide, heavy showers could be on the way.

Hail

Listen out for these pellets of solid ice falling noisily on thundery days. They can be all sizes – sometimes even as big as ice cubes!

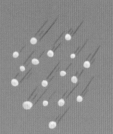

Hair-like strands at the top

Cumulonimbus capillatus

The top of this towering storm cloud could be more than 18km (11 miles) above the ground. You'll be able to see it best if it's far away.

Lightning

If you see bright crackles
of lightning in the sky on
a stormy day, listen for the
rumble of thunder, too.

Cumulonimbus calvus

Another tall storm cloud that
hangs low in the sky. This
one has smooth bumps along
the top, rather than strands.

Beams of light split
into different shades

Rainbow

Look for rainbows forming
after showers, when sunlight
shines through water
droplets in the air.

Cloudy days

Undulatus

Just like waves on water, these ripples of cloud show the patterns of the air currents blowing high in the sky.

Look for it hiding the tops of tall buildings or trees

Stratus nebulosus

A very low, thick cloud. When it's low enough to touch the ground, it is usually called fog.

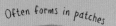

Often forms in patches

Mist

Look out for mist on a chilly morning. It will probably disappear as the sun warms the ground.

Altostratus

This dull, flat cloud
can cover the whole sky.
It might bring light,
drizzly rain with it.

Fog

You'll see fog in winter,
especially after a cold, clear
night. It's much thicker than
mist, and harder to see through.

*Also called
cloud streets*

Radiatus

When the wind's blowing
high up, you might see
clouds stretching in
long, straight lines.

Winter weather

Very high up in the sky

Cirrocumulus stratiformis

Look for these tiny, fleecy clouds stretching across the whole sky. They can mean that bad weather is coming.

Ground frost

This layer of ice forms on the ground on cold nights. Listen for the crunch as you walk across frosty grass.

Usually forms in clear skies

Diamond dust

You might spot these tiny ice crystals sparkling in the air on an extremely cold day.

Snowflakes

Try looking closely at snowflakes that have fallen on your coat or hat to see their beautiful shapes.

Made from ice crystals that join up in the clouds

Snow grains

Each one is no bigger than a grain of sand. Look for them falling in flurries on chilly days.

Rime

You might see trees or plants covered in this ice. It's formed when the water droplets in fog freeze and cling to the branches.

Looks like icy needles up close

9

Rainy days

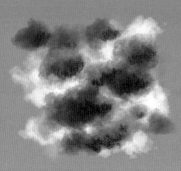

Stratocumulus stratiformis

These low, clumpy clouds cover the sky, and might bring drizzle. Look for the different shapes within them.

Can bring snow in winter

Nimbostratus

Don't forget your umbrella if you see this thick, dark layer of cloud – heavy rain is probably on the way.

May be wet, or very icy

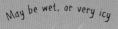

Sleet

Watch out for this mixture of rain and snow on winter days. Warmer air closer to the ground melts the snowflakes as they fall.

Stratus fractus

Try and spot these wispy clouds floating beneath other clouds, often moving fast.

Rain

When water droplets in the clouds join together and get too heavy, they fall to the ground as rain. Have fun splashing in the puddles!

Altocumulus castellanus

The tops of these clouds rise in fluffy peaks, like the battlements of a castle.

Might mean that storms are coming

11

Sunrise and sunset

Altocumulus stratiformis

A thin, clumpy layer that can stretch far across the sky. As the daylight fades, the clouds might start to glow red, pink or gold.

Duplicatus

Sometimes two layers of clouds such as cirrus, cirrostratus or altocumulus can form at different heights.

Similar to altostratus (page 7) but much higher and thinner

Cirrostratus

This filmy layer of ice crystals can be very pale and nearly see-through. You might see it covering much of the sky.

Circumzenithal arc

Look straight up above your head when the sun is close to the horizon to try and spot this rainbow-like curve.

Can be over 80km (50 miles) from the ground

Noctilucent clouds

The highest clouds in the Earth's atmosphere. Look for them on clear summer nights just after sunset.

Sun pillar

Watch for this shining streak above or below the sun as it's rising or setting. It's caused by sunlight bouncing off ice crystals in the air.

Unusual clouds

Sometimes called
Kelvin-Helmholtz waves

Fluctus

These regular curls form
along the tops of clouds
and look like breaking
waves on water.

Horseshoe vortex

You'll have to be sharp-eyed
to spot this little loop of cloud
– it usually only lasts for
about a minute.

Looks a bit like a UFO

Lenticular clouds

Named after lentils because
of their smooth, rounded shape.
You might see one by itself, or
a few piled up like plates.

Nacreous clouds

Look for these glowing
pastel clouds in cold
weather, when the sun is
just below the horizon.

*Can be caused by planes
flying through clouds*

Fallstreak hole

Also called a hole-punch cloud.
Part of a cloud suddenly freezes
and begins to fall as high-up
rain or snow.

Arcus

Watch for this long
tube of cloud rolling
across the sky on
a stormy day.

*Looks dark
and low*

Cloud features

Can stay for a long time

Velum

You might spot this long, thin strip near large cumulonimbus or cumulus clouds.

Pileus

Look for this smooth cap of cloud on top of another cloud. It can also form over a mountain peak.

Dark and ragged-looking

Pannus

Watch for them hovering beneath other clouds. They're usually a warning that rain or snow will soon start to fall.

Mamma

Pouchy bumps that hang down from the bottom of clouds. You might notice them after a storm.

Virga

If you see these hanging trails, it means it's raining or snowing high up in the sky – but it won't reach the ground.

Can sometimes touch the ground

Tuba

You might see a thin funnel like this stretching down from the base of a storm cloud. It's formed by swirling winds.

Other clouds

Contrails

Watch on a clear day for these aircraft trails slashing straight across the sky.

Can stay in the sky for hours

Also called pyrocumulus

Flammogenitus

These huge, ashy clouds rise into the air above wildfires and volcanic eruptions.

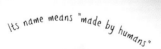

Its name means "made by humans"

Homogenitus

Any man-made cloud, such as the ones you might spot billowing from power stations or factories.

18

Silvagenitus

Look for this cloud above forests. It's caused by tiny droplets of water leaving the trees' leaves.

Cataractagenitus

You'll often see misty clouds rising above big waterfalls – see if you can feel the moisture in the air.

Banner cloud

Caused by wind blowing around mountaintops. It looks like a flag flying from a peak.

Light effects

Corona

You might spot this effect when a thin layer of cloud is covering the sun or moon.

Glory

You're most likely to see one from a plane window. Look for the plane's shadow in the middle.

Usually seen when the sun is behind you

Fogbow

Like a rainbow, but it appears in fog or mist. It's so pale that it looks white.

Crepuscular rays

Look for these beams
of light shining down
between gaps in the
clouds like spotlights.

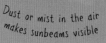

*Dust or mist in the air
makes sunbeams visible*

*Wide ring around
the sun or moon*

Halo

You might see a halo when
light shines through the ice
crystals of high-up clouds.

Iridescence

Thin clouds can shimmer
with pastel shades when the
sun shines through them.

Spotting chart

Once you've spotted something from this book, find its sticker at the back, and stick it on this chart in the space below its name.

Altocumulus castellanus	Altocumulus stratiformis	Altostratus	Arcus	Banner cloud
Cataracta-genitus	Circumzenithal arc	Cirrocumulus stratiformis	Cirrostratus	Cirrus floccus
Cirrus uncinus	Contrails	Corona	Crepuscular rays	Cumulonimbus calvus
Cumulonimbus capillatus	Cumulus congestus	Cumulus fractus	Cumulus humilis	Cumulus mediocris
Diamond dust	Duplicatus	Fallstreak holes	Flammogenitus	Fluctus

Fog	Fogbow	Glory	Ground frost	Hail
Halo	Homogenitus	Horseshoe vortex	Iridescence	Lenticular clouds
Lightning	Mamma	Mist	Nacreous clouds	Nimbostratus
Noctilucent clouds	Pannus	Pileus	Radiatus	Rain
Rainbow	Rime	Silvagenitus	Sleet	Snowflakes
Snow grains	Stratocumulus stratiformis	Stratus fractus	Stratus nebulosus	Sun
Sun pillar	Tuba	Undulatus	Velum	Virga

Index

First published in 2022 by Usborne Publishing Ltd, Usborne House, 83-85 Saffron Hill, London EC1N 8RT, England. usborne.com
Copyright © 2022 Usborne Publishing Ltd. The name Usborne and the Balloon logo are trade marks of Usborne Publishing Ltd.
All rights reserved. No part of this publication may be reproduced, stored in a retrieval system or transmitted in
any form or by any means without the prior permission of the publisher. Printed in China. UE.